# Con

C000115680

# The First Disciples

John, the Baptist, preached as usual. He told the people to repent from their evil ways and turn to God. He preached to them about the Messiah, whom God had sent to save the people from their sins. He said that God had sent him as a messenger to make the way ready for the Messiah to come.

The next day, John, the Baptist, was standing

with his two disciples, when he saw Jesus walking by. John exclaimed, "Look! The Lamb of God!" Hearing this, both John's disciples followed Jesus, walking behind him.

Jesus noticed them. He turned to them and asked, "What are you looking for?"

They replied, "Master, where do you live?"

Then, Jesus invited them, "Come and see!" They went with him, and spent the day with him.

Now, one of the disciples who followed Jesus was Andrew. When he went back home, he met his brother Simon and said, "We have found the Messiah, the Christ, God's Anointed One, the very one that John, the Baptist, told us about!"

Andrew then brought Simon to Jesus.

Jesus, looking at Simon, said, "You are Simon, son of Jona. Hereafter, you shall be called Cephas, which means 'Stone'."

# Jesus Chooses Twelve Disciples

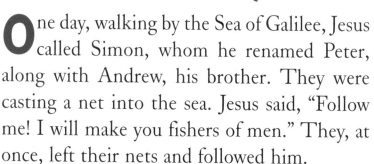

One day, walking by the Sea of Galilee, Jesus called Simon, whom he renamed Peter, along with Andrew, his brother. They were casting a net into the sea. Jesus said, "Follow me! I will make you fishers of men." They, at once, left their nets and followed him.

A little later, Jesus saw two other fishermen, James and John, the sons of Zebedee, on their father's ship, mending their fishing nets. Jesus called them, too, to follow him. Immediately, they too left everything and followed Jesus.

The next day, Jesus saw Philip and said, "Follow me."

Altogether, Jesus chose twelve disciples. They were always with him, learning from him and doing some of the things he did.

Jesus then called Matthew, the tax collector, who was sitting at his place of work collecting

taxes. Matthew simply left the place where he worked and followed Jesus. Besides these, Jesus chose Thomas, Bartholomew, James, the son of Alphaeus, Thaddeus (also called Judas, brother of James) and Simon, the zealot.

Judas Iscariot, who also lived closely with Jesus just like the other disciples, was given charge of the disciples' money. He was a dishonest man. It was he who finally betrayed Jesus.

# The First Miracle

**I**n a certain place called Cana in Galilee, there was a wedding. Jesus, his disciples and Mary, the mother of Jesus were invited.

The wine got over! Mary came to Jesus, telling him about the unexpected lack of wine. Jesus

replied, "Why do you involve me? My time has not yet come." But, Mary told the servants to do exactly what Jesus instructed them.

Jesus told the servants to fill six stone jars with water. The jars were filled to the brim. The water in these jars was supposed to be used by the Jews to wash their hands and feet, according to their ceremonial custom. Then, Jesus asked the servants to serve some of that water to the host of the wedding.

The host tasted the water. It had turned into wine! He did not know where it had come from. But the servants knew, since they had filled the jars with water.

The host called the bridegroom aside and said, "Everyone serves the best wine first, and the cheaper variety later, after the guests have had much to drink. But you have saved the best till now!"

This was the first miracle that Jesus performed. The disciples witnessed this and believed him.

# Man with the Evil Spirit

Jesus arrived at Capernaum with his disciples. On the Sabbath, which is the seventh day of the week, Jesus went to the synagogue. There were a lot of people gathered there. Jesus began teaching in the synagogue. The people who heard him were amazed. They had not heard anyone speak so confidently, with authority and power. The teachers of Law usually did not teach so clearly.

Just then, a man who had an evil spirit within him, came to the synagogue. He recognised Jesus and shouted, "What do you want from us, you, Jesus of Nazareth? I know you have come to destroy us. I know who you are, the Holy One of God!"

Jesus turned to him and spoke sternly to the evil spirit, "Be quiet, and come out of him." The evil spirit shook up the man violently and gave a loud shriek and left his body.

The people who watched this were astonished. They had never seen anything like this before. They spoke among themselves saying that this was a new teaching, for Jesus commanded an evil spirit to obey him with great authority!

News about Jesus spread quickly all over Galilee.

# Jesus Heals Peter's Mother-in-Law

**O**ne day, Jesus and his disciples, Andrew, James and John returned from the synagogue after worship. They went to Simon Peter's house to see him. At that time, Peter's wife's mother was ill. She had high fever and was in bed.

After talking for a while, Peter told Jesus that

his mother-in-law was not well.

So, Jesus went to the room where she was lying down. He held her hand and woke her up. At once, the fever left her body! She got up feeling completely well. Immediately, she went inside and started getting things ready for the guests to eat!

Everyone who heard about this was amazed. They had never seen anyone with high fever recover so quickly.

By the evening, as the sun was setting, those living nearby brought all those who were ill with various diseases, right up to Peter's door! Even those who were possessed with evil spirits were brought to Jesus. It seemed like the entire city was gathered around Peter's house!

Thus, Jesus healed many people suffering from different kinds of illnesses. He cast out many evil spirits that had been troubling the people. However, he commanded the evil spirits not to speak, because they knew who he was.

# Jesus Visits Nazareth

Jesus continued doing the work God had sent him to do. Everyone spoke about him. Wherever he went, he taught in the synagogue and everyone who heard him was amazed by his wisdom.

Once, Jesus went to Nazareth, his hometown. On the seventh day, on Sabbath, Jesus went as usual to the synagogue. In the synagogue, he read from a scroll, the words of Prophet Isaiah. Then, he rolled up the scroll and gave it to an attendant and sat down. People continued to look at him. Jesus said, "Today, that would be all. What I have just read is enough."

The people spoke about Jesus, saying, "Isn't he Joseph's son?"

Jesus told them, "I am sure you will ask me to perform the same miracles here that I did in Capernaum." Then, he explained. The people had seen him grow up in Nazareth. Now it would be difficult for them to accept him as

the one God had chosen to be the Messiah.

The people became angry with what Jesus said. They actually chased him out of the town and even wanted to push him over the hill! But, Jesus simply walked through the middle of the crowd and disappeared.

13

# John is Imprisoned

**J**ohn, the Baptist, was sent as a messenger to prepare the people to accept Jesus as their Saviour.

John had his own disciples. He had led many people to repentance and had baptised them. He had also baptised Jesus. John became so popular that people wondered if he was the

Messiah. He clearly said that he was not Christ, but was sent ahead of him.

John lived during King Herod's rule. Now, Herod had married Herodias, his brother, Philip's wife. John told Herod that what he had done was wrong in God's sight. John also did not approve of the other evils Herod was doing.

Although Herod hated John, he did not dare to harm him. Herod knew John was a holy man and he liked listening to him. But one day, he threw John in prison. Now, John could not continue his work.

John's disciples were disturbed. They asked Jesus whether he was truly the Messiah or if they should wait for someone else. Jesus told them to go back and tell John all the miracles they saw Jesus do. John was happy when his disciples told him about Jesus' doings.

Then, Jesus told his disciples that John was the greatest man who ever lived.

# Reward for a Dance

It was King Herod's birthday and a big banquet was arranged for all the high officials, military commanders and leading men.

Herodias, King Herod's wife, hated John, the Baptist. She really wanted to kill him, but could not do so without the authority of Herod.

King Herod had actually thrown John in prison for Herodias' sake!

At the birthday banquet, Herodias' daughter danced before the guests. Herod was so pleased that he promised to give her whatever she requested, even half of his kingdom.

The daughter consulted Herodias, her mother.

Then, she asked Herod to give her John, the Baptist's, head on a plate.

King Herod was very upset, but he had promised to give whatever she asked. He ordered the executioners to behead John.

They did so and brought John's head on a platter. Herod presented it to the daughter and she gave it to her mother. Everyone was shocked.

Elsewhere, people were talking about the miracles Jesus was doing. Some thought he was John who had come back from the dead. Herod, too, thought the same!

17

# The Sermon on the Mount

Jesus saw a large crowd following him. So, he climbed up a mountainside and sat down. Then, he taught his disciples what are also known as the Beatitudes.

God blesses certain types of people with particular attitudes!

The poor who realise they need God are promised that the Kingdom of Heaven belongs to them. God Himself will comfort those who mourn and grieve. The humble and contented ones will own the Earth.

Those who are passionate for Godly things will receive deep satisfaction from following after them.

Care and mercy will be shown to those who are merciful and caring.

Those who keep their hearts and minds clean will surely see God.

Those who work for peace will find their place in the family of God as His children.

Those who are persecuted for following after Godly things will belong to the Kingdom of Heaven.

Finally, Jesus said that the disciples should consider themselves blessed when men will put them down, say lies and bad things about them, because they are His followers.

He encouraged them by saying, "Be happy and rejoice about all this, because a great reward awaits you in Heaven. The ancient prophets, too, were persecuted just like this."

# The Light of the World

On another day, Jesus went up a mountainside and sat down. Then, he began teaching his disciples. He was explaining to them the usefulness and importance of salt and light.

Salt adds flavour to food and light helps us to see.

Jesus first told the people that they are the salt of the Earth. If the salt loses its flavour, it becomes useless, and is fit only to be thrown down and trampled under the feet of men! So, the disciples were instructed to be a blessing among the people.

Then, he told the disciples that they were the light of the world. A city, which is built on a hill, cannot be hidden. Everyone can see it.

A lamp gives light when it is lit. It is never kept under a bowl. Instead, it should be kept on a stand so that it can burn and give out

light to everyone. This way all that is good and bad can be seen.

Jesus told the disciples to be such lights in the world.

He also said that the disciples were to live such lives that people would see their good works and praise God, our Father in Heaven.

# Jesus Teaches about Prayer

**O**nce, Jesus was teaching his disciples about true prayer. First, he told them how not to pray.

There are some who pretend to be good and honourable but are really not so. These kind of

people like to stand and pray in public places, for everyone to see them.

Then, Jesus taught his disciples the right way to pray. They were to close the door of their room and pray in secret to God, the Father.

Then, as God sees how honestly they pray in secret, He will openly reward them before everyone.

Jesus also told the disciples not to say long prayers with unwanted or repetitive words. God, our Father, knows what we need even before we ask Him.

Then, Jesus taught them a pattern of prayer, which today is commonly called the Lord's Prayer: "Our Father in Heaven, blessed is your name. Your kingdom come, yours will be done on Earth as it is in Heaven. Give us today our daily bread. Forgive us our sins, as we forgive those who have sinned against us. Lead us not into temptation. But deliver us from the evil one. For yours is the kingdom, the power and the glory forever. Amen."

# The Two Prayers

**J**esus told another parable, or story, to some people who always thought they were much better or holier than others. These people usually looked down on the ordinary people.

Once, there were two men who went to the Temple to pray. One was a teacher of the law and the other was a collector of tax.

The teacher of the law stood up, praying loudly, for himself. He looked up towards Heaven and said, "Oh God, I thank you that I am not like other people - dishonest, greedy, unfaithful in marriage, and particularly not like this tax collector. I fast twice a week and give tax on all my income."

The tax collector stood at a distance. He struck his chest, sorry for the wrong he had done. He did not think he was good enough to even look up to Heaven. This man prayed, saying, "God, have mercy on me. Forgive me, for I am a sinner."

Then, Jesus remarked, "The tax collector got blessed by God before he went home, but the teacher of law did not." Jesus further explained that anyone who is proud will always be brought down, whereas, God would always lift up the humble.

# A Friend Visits at Midnight

**J**esus was teaching about prayer. He told this story to show how prayer works.

"At midnight, if your friend visits you after a long journey and you realise there is no bread to offer him, what would you do? You would go to another friend's house to borrow bread. That friend could say that he is already in bed with his family, the door is locked and he did not want to be disturbed. He may not get up. But he will surely get out of bed and give you what you ask only if you are persistent in asking."

So, Jesus affirmed that if anyone asks, he would surely receive. When anyone seeks, he will find what he is looking for and when he knocks, the door will definitely be opened.

Then, Jesus addressed the fathers, "If your children ask you for a fish, will you give them

a snake instead? If they ask for an egg, will you give a scorpion? Earthly fathers know how to give good gifts to their children. Our Heavenly Father will certainly give the Holy Spirit to those who ask Him."

# The Two Builders

Crowds of people followed Jesus wherever he went. Most often, they would hear his teachings and go away. Jesus wanted the people to understand and put into practice all that they heard him teach.

He said that those who hear his words and obey them are wise, whereas those who simply hear his teachings and do not put them into practice are foolish.

Jesus gave the example of a wise man and a foolish man. The wise man is the one who built his house on a rock. The foundation of his house was strong and firm. One day, it rained and the water rose; the winds blew and beat against the house. But, that house stood firm, as the foundation was on solid rock.

The foolish man also built a house. But, he built his house on sand. The foundation of his house was not strong and firm. Then, the rains came and the water rose; the winds

blew and beat against the house. That house crashed to the ground.

Jesus was comparing the house to people and the storm to the problems of life. Only those people whose foundation is God, will not be shaken by problems.

# Four Friends
# Make a Way

**O**nce, Jesus was teaching in a certain house at Capernaum. The house became very crowded as people rushed in to hear him! Four men came carrying a paralysed man on a mat. They tried to take him inside for Jesus to heal

him. As they could not carry him through the door, they took off the roof tiles and lowered him down the roof. They laid him in the middle of the crowd, in front of Jesus. Seeing the men's faith, Jesus told the paralysed man, "Son, your sins are forgiven."

The teachers of the law heard this and wondered among themselves who Jesus really was. They knew only God can forgive sins, and to them Jesus was just another man.

Jesus knew their thoughts and asked them, "Is it not easier to say 'Your sins are forgiven', rather than saying 'Get up and walk'?" Then, he informed them that the Son of Man had the right on Earth to forgive sins.

Turning to the man, he said, "Take your mat and go home."

The Man immediately took his mat and went home praising God. Everyone who saw this miracle was surprised, as they had never seen such a thing before.

# Also available in the 15 Stories series

## Aesop's Fables (Set of 48 books)